HAYDEN MᶜNEIL

EXP. NUMBER	EXPERIMENT/SUBJECT		DATE	
NAME		LAB PARTNER	LOCKER/DESK NO.	COURSE & SECTION NO.

SIGNATURE	DATE	WITNESS/TA	DATE

NOTE: INSERT DIVIDER UNDER COPY SHEET BEFORE WRITING

EXP. NUMBER	EXPERIMENT/SUBJECT		DATE		08
NAME		LAB PARTNER	LOCKER/DESK NO.	COURSE & SECTION NO.	

COPY

SIGNATURE	DATE	WITNESS/TA	DATE

THE HAYDEN-McNEIL STUDENT LAB NOTEBOOK

NOTE: INSERT DIVIDER UNDER COPY SHEET BEFORE WRITING

EXP. NUMBER	EXPERIMENT/SUBJECT		DATE	
NAME		LAB PARTNER	LOCKER/DESK NO.	COURSE & SECTION NO.

SIGNATURE		DATE	WITNESS/TA	DATE

EXP. NUMBER	EXPERIMENT/SUBJECT		DATE	
NAME		LAB PARTNER	LOCKER/DESK NO.	COURSE & SECTION NO.

SIGNATURE		DATE	WITNESS/TA		DATE

THE HAYDEN-McNEIL STUDENT LAB NOTEBOOK

NOTE: INSERT DIVIDER UNDER COPY SHEET BEFORE WRITING

EXP. NUMBER	EXPERIMENT/SUBJECT		DATE	
NAME		LAB PARTNER	LOCKER/DESK NO.	COURSE & SECTION NO.

SIGNATURE	DATE	WITNESS/TA	DATE

EXP. NUMBER	EXPERIMENT/SUBJECT		DATE	
NAME		LAB PARTNER	LOCKER/DESK NO.	COURSE & SECTION NO.

SIGNATURE	DATE	WITNESS/TA		DATE

NOTE: INSERT DIVIDER UNDER COPY SHEET BEFORE WRITING

EXP. NUMBER	EXPERIMENT/SUBJECT		DATE	
NAME		LAB PARTNER	LOCKER/DESK NO.	COURSE & SECTION NO.

SIGNATURE	DATE	WITNESS/TA	DATE

NOTE: INSERT DIVIDER UNDER COPY SHEET BEFORE WRITING

EXP. NUMBER	EXPERIMENT/SUBJECT		DATE		11
NAME		LAB PARTNER	LOCKER/DESK NO.	COURSE & SECTION NO.	

SIGNATURE		DATE	WITNESS/TA		DATE

THE HAYDEN-McNEIL STUDENT LAB NOTEBOOK

NOTE: INSERT DIVIDER UNDER COPY SHEET BEFORE WRITING

EXP. NUMBER	EXPERIMENT/SUBJECT		DATE	
NAME		LAB PARTNER	LOCKER/DESK NO.	COURSE & SECTION NO.

SIGNATURE	DATE	WITNESS/TA		DATE

NOTE: INSERT DIVIDER UNDER COPY SHEET BEFORE WRITING

EXP. NUMBER	EXPERIMENT/SUBJECT		DATE	
NAME		LAB PARTNER	LOCKER/DESK NO.	COURSE & SECTION NO.

SIGNATURE		DATE	WITNESS/TA		DATE

NOTE: INSERT DIVIDER UNDER COPY SHEET BEFORE WRITING

EXP. NUMBER	EXPERIMENT/SUBJECT		DATE	
NAME		LAB PARTNER	LOCKER/DESK NO.	COURSE & SECTION NO.

SIGNATURE	DATE	WITNESS/TA	DATE

THE HAYDEN-McNEIL STUDENT LAB NOTEBOOK

NOTE: INSERT DIVIDER UNDER COPY SHEET BEFORE WRITING

EXP. NUMBER	EXPERIMENT/SUBJECT		DATE		14
NAME		LAB PARTNER	LOCKER/DESK NO.	COURSE & SECTION NO.	

SIGNATURE		DATE	WITNESS/TA		DATE

NOTE: INSERT DIVIDER UNDER COPY SHEET BEFORE WRITING

EXP. NUMBER	EXPERIMENT/SUBJECT		DATE	
NAME		LAB PARTNER	LOCKER/DESK NO.	COURSE & SECTION NO.

SIGNATURE	DATE	WITNESS/TA	DATE

NOTE: INSERT DIVIDER UNDER COPY SHEET BEFORE WRITING

EXP. NUMBER	EXPERIMENT/SUBJECT		DATE		16
NAME		LAB PARTNER	LOCKER/DESK NO.	COURSE & SECTION NO.	

SIGNATURE		DATE	WITNESS/TA		DATE

THE HAYDEN-McNEIL STUDENT LAB NOTEBOOK

NOTE: INSERT DIVIDER UNDER COPY SHEET BEFORE WRITING

EXP. NUMBER	EXPERIMENT/SUBJECT		DATE	
NAME		LAB PARTNER	LOCKER/DESK NO.	COURSE & SECTION NO.

SIGNATURE		DATE	WITNESS/TA		DATE

NOTE: INSERT DIVIDER UNDER COPY SHEET BEFORE WRITING

EXP. NUMBER	EXPERIMENT/SUBJECT		DATE	
NAME		LAB PARTNER	LOCKER/DESK NO.	COURSE & SECTION NO.

SIGNATURE	DATE	WITNESS/TA	DATE

NOTE: INSERT DIVIDER UNDER COPY SHEET BEFORE WRITING

EXP. NUMBER	EXPERIMENT/SUBJECT		DATE	
NAME		LAB PARTNER	LOCKER/DESK NO.	COURSE & SECTION NO.

SIGNATURE		DATE	WITNESS/TA		DATE

NOTE: INSERT DIVIDER UNDER COPY SHEET BEFORE WRITING

EXP. NUMBER	EXPERIMENT/SUBJECT		DATE	
NAME		LAB PARTNER	LOCKER/DESK NO.	COURSE & SECTION NO.

SIGNATURE		DATE	WITNESS/TA		DATE

THE HAYDEN-McNEIL STUDENT LAB NOTEBOOK

NOTE: INSERT DIVIDER UNDER COPY SHEET BEFORE WRITING

EXP. NUMBER	EXPERIMENT/SUBJECT		DATE	20
NAME		LAB PARTNER	LOCKER/DESK NO.	COURSE & SECTION NO.

COPY

SIGNATURE		DATE	WITNESS/TA		DATE

THE HAYDEN-McNEIL STUDENT LAB NOTEBOOK

NOTE: INSERT DIVIDER UNDER COPY SHEET BEFORE WRITING

EXP. NUMBER	EXPERIMENT/SUBJECT		DATE	
NAME		LAB PARTNER	LOCKER/DESK NO.	COURSE & SECTION NO.

SIGNATURE	DATE	WITNESS/TA	DATE

NOTE: INSERT DIVIDER UNDER COPY SHEET BEFORE WRITING

EXP. NUMBER	EXPERIMENT/SUBJECT		DATE	
NAME		LAB PARTNER	LOCKER/DESK NO.	COURSE & SECTION NO.

SIGNATURE		DATE	WITNESS/TA		DATE

NOTE: INSERT DIVIDER UNDER COPY SHEET BEFORE WRITING

EXP. NUMBER	EXPERIMENT/SUBJECT		DATE	
NAME		LAB PARTNER	LOCKER/DESK NO.	COURSE & SECTION NO.

SIGNATURE		DATE	WITNESS/TA		DATE

NOTE: INSERT DIVIDER UNDER COPY SHEET BEFORE WRITING

EXP. NUMBER	EXPERIMENT/SUBJECT		DATE		22
NAME		LAB PARTNER	LOCKER/DESK NO.	COURSE & SECTION NO.	

SIGNATURE	DATE	WITNESS/TA		DATE

NOTE: INSERT DIVIDER UNDER COPY SHEET BEFORE WRITING

EXP. NUMBER	EXPERIMENT/SUBJECT		DATE	
NAME		LAB PARTNER	LOCKER/DESK NO.	COURSE & SECTION NO.

SIGNATURE	DATE	WITNESS/TA	DATE

THE HAYDEN-McNEIL STUDENT LAB NOTEBOOK

NOTE: INSERT DIVIDER UNDER COPY SHEET BEFORE WRITING

EXP. NUMBER	EXPERIMENT/SUBJECT		DATE	
NAME		LAB PARTNER	LOCKER/DESK NO.	COURSE & SECTION NO.

SIGNATURE	DATE	WITNESS/TA	DATE

THE HAYDEN-McNEIL STUDENT LAB NOTEBOOK

NOTE: INSERT DIVIDER UNDER COPY SHEET BEFORE WRITING

EXP. NUMBER	EXPERIMENT/SUBJECT		DATE	
NAME		LAB PARTNER	LOCKER/DESK NO.	COURSE & SECTION NO.

SIGNATURE		DATE	WITNESS/TA		DATE

NOTE: INSERT DIVIDER UNDER COPY SHEET BEFORE WRITING

EXP. NUMBER	EXPERIMENT/SUBJECT		DATE	
NAME		LAB PARTNER	LOCKER/DESK NO.	COURSE & SECTION NO.

SIGNATURE		DATE	WITNESS/TA		DATE

NOTE: INSERT DIVIDER UNDER COPY SHEET BEFORE WRITING

EXP. NUMBER	EXPERIMENT/SUBJECT		DATE	26
NAME		LAB PARTNER	LOCKER/DESK NO.	COURSE & SECTION NO.

SIGNATURE	DATE	WITNESS/TA		DATE

THE HAYDEN-McNEIL STUDENT LAB NOTEBOOK

NOTE: INSERT DIVIDER UNDER COPY SHEET BEFORE WRITING

EXP. NUMBER	EXPERIMENT/SUBJECT		DATE	
NAME		LAB PARTNER	LOCKER/DESK NO.	COURSE & SECTION NO.

SIGNATURE	DATE	WITNESS/TA	DATE

NOTE: INSERT DIVIDER UNDER COPY SHEET BEFORE WRITING

EXP. NUMBER	EXPERIMENT/SUBJECT		DATE	
NAME		LAB PARTNER	LOCKER/DESK NO.	COURSE & SECTION NO.

SIGNATURE		DATE	WITNESS/TA		DATE

NOTE: INSERT DIVIDER UNDER COPY SHEET BEFORE WRITING

EXP. NUMBER	EXPERIMENT/SUBJECT		DATE	
NAME		LAB PARTNER	LOCKER/DESK NO.	COURSE & SECTION NO.

SIGNATURE	DATE	WITNESS/TA	DATE

NOTE: INSERT DIVIDER UNDER COPY SHEET BEFORE WRITING

EXP. NUMBER	EXPERIMENT/SUBJECT		DATE		28
NAME		LAB PARTNER	LOCKER/DESK NO.	COURSE & SECTION NO.	

SIGNATURE	DATE	WITNESS/TA	DATE

NOTE: INSERT DIVIDER UNDER COPY SHEET BEFORE WRITING

EXP. NUMBER	EXPERIMENT/SUBJECT		DATE	
NAME		LAB PARTNER	LOCKER/DESK NO.	COURSE & SECTION NO.

SIGNATURE		DATE	WITNESS/TA		DATE

NOTE: INSERT DIVIDER UNDER COPY SHEET BEFORE WRITING

EXP. NUMBER	EXPERIMENT/SUBJECT		DATE	
NAME		LAB PARTNER	LOCKER/DESK NO.	COURSE & SECTION NO.

SIGNATURE		DATE	WITNESS/TA		DATE

THE HAYDEN-McNEIL STUDENT LAB NOTEBOOK

NOTE: INSERT DIVIDER UNDER COPY SHEET BEFORE WRITING

EXP. NUMBER	EXPERIMENT/SUBJECT		DATE	
NAME		LAB PARTNER	LOCKER/DESK NO.	COURSE & SECTION NO.

SIGNATURE	DATE	WITNESS/TA	DATE

NOTE: INSERT DIVIDER UNDER COPY SHEET BEFORE WRITING

EXP. NUMBER	EXPERIMENT/SUBJECT		DATE	
NAME		LAB PARTNER	LOCKER/DESK NO.	COURSE & SECTION NO.

SIGNATURE		DATE	WITNESS/TA		DATE

EXP. NUMBER	EXPERIMENT/SUBJECT		DATE	
NAME		LAB PARTNER	LOCKER/DESK NO.	COURSE & SECTION NO.

SIGNATURE	DATE	WITNESS/TA	DATE

EXP. NUMBER	EXPERIMENT/SUBJECT		DATE	
NAME		LAB PARTNER	LOCKER/DESK NO.	COURSE & SECTION NO.

SIGNATURE		DATE	WITNESS/TA		DATE

NOTE: INSERT DIVIDER UNDER COPY SHEET BEFORE WRITING

EXP. NUMBER	EXPERIMENT/SUBJECT		DATE	
NAME		LAB PARTNER	LOCKER/DESK NO.	COURSE & SECTION NO.

SIGNATURE		DATE	WITNESS/TA		DATE

NOTE: INSERT DIVIDER UNDER COPY SHEET BEFORE WRITING

EXP. NUMBER	EXPERIMENT/SUBJECT		DATE	
NAME		LAB PARTNER	LOCKER/DESK NO.	COURSE & SECTION NO.

SIGNATURE		DATE	WITNESS/TA		DATE

THE HAYDEN-McNEIL STUDENT LAB NOTEBOOK

NOTE: INSERT DIVIDER UNDER COPY SHEET BEFORE WRITING

EXP. NUMBER	EXPERIMENT/SUBJECT		DATE	
NAME		LAB PARTNER	LOCKER/DESK NO.	COURSE & SECTION NO.

SIGNATURE	DATE	WITNESS/TA	DATE

EXP. NUMBER	EXPERIMENT/SUBJECT		DATE	34
NAME		LAB PARTNER	LOCKER/DESK NO.	COURSE & SECTION NO.

COPY

SIGNATURE	DATE	WITNESS/TA		DATE

NOTE: INSERT DIVIDER UNDER COPY SHEET BEFORE WRITING

EXP. NUMBER	EXPERIMENT/SUBJECT		DATE	
NAME		LAB PARTNER	LOCKER/DESK NO.	COURSE & SECTION NO.

SIGNATURE		DATE	WITNESS/TA		DATE

NOTE: INSERT DIVIDER UNDER COPY SHEET BEFORE WRITING

EXP. NUMBER	EXPERIMENT/SUBJECT		DATE	
NAME		LAB PARTNER	LOCKER/DESK NO.	COURSE & SECTION NO.

SIGNATURE		DATE	WITNESS/TA		DATE

NOTE: INSERT DIVIDER UNDER COPY SHEET BEFORE WRITING

EXP. NUMBER	EXPERIMENT/SUBJECT		DATE	
NAME		LAB PARTNER	LOCKER/DESK NO.	COURSE & SECTION NO.

SIGNATURE		DATE	WITNESS/TA		DATE

THE HAYDEN-McNEIL STUDENT LAB NOTEBOOK

NOTE: INSERT DIVIDER UNDER COPY SHEET BEFORE WRITING

EXP. NUMBER	EXPERIMENT/SUBJECT		DATE	
NAME		LAB PARTNER	LOCKER/DESK NO.	COURSE & SECTION NO.

SIGNATURE		DATE	WITNESS/TA		DATE

NOTE: INSERT DIVIDER UNDER COPY SHEET BEFORE WRITING

EXP. NUMBER	EXPERIMENT/SUBJECT		DATE	
NAME		LAB PARTNER	LOCKER/DESK NO.	COURSE & SECTION NO.

SIGNATURE		DATE	WITNESS/TA		DATE

NOTE: INSERT DIVIDER UNDER COPY SHEET BEFORE WRITING

EXP. NUMBER	EXPERIMENT/SUBJECT		DATE	
NAME		LAB PARTNER	LOCKER/DESK NO.	COURSE & SECTION NO.

SIGNATURE		DATE	WITNESS/TA		DATE

NOTE: INSERT DIVIDER UNDER COPY SHEET BEFORE WRITING

EXP. NUMBER	EXPERIMENT/SUBJECT		DATE	
NAME		LAB PARTNER	LOCKER/DESK NO.	COURSE & SECTION NO.

SIGNATURE		DATE	WITNESS/TA		DATE

NOTE: INSERT DIVIDER UNDER COPY SHEET BEFORE WRITING

EXP. NUMBER	EXPERIMENT/SUBJECT		DATE	
NAME		LAB PARTNER	LOCKER/DESK NO.	COURSE & SECTION NO.

COPY

SIGNATURE	DATE	WITNESS/TA	DATE

NOTE: INSERT DIVIDER UNDER COPY SHEET BEFORE WRITING

EXP. NUMBER	EXPERIMENT/SUBJECT		DATE	
NAME		LAB PARTNER	LOCKER/DESK NO.	COURSE & SECTION NO.

SIGNATURE		DATE	WITNESS/TA		DATE

THE HAYDEN-McNEIL STUDENT LAB NOTEBOOK

NOTE: INSERT DIVIDER UNDER COPY SHEET BEFORE WRITING

EXP. NUMBER	EXPERIMENT/SUBJECT		DATE	
NAME		LAB PARTNER	LOCKER/DESK NO.	COURSE & SECTION NO.

SIGNATURE		DATE	WITNESS/TA		DATE

NOTE: INSERT DIVIDER UNDER COPY SHEET BEFORE WRITING

EXP. NUMBER	EXPERIMENT/SUBJECT		DATE	41
NAME		LAB PARTNER	LOCKER/DESK NO.	COURSE & SECTION NO.

SIGNATURE	DATE	WITNESS/TA	DATE

EXP. NUMBER	EXPERIMENT/SUBJECT		DATE	
NAME		LAB PARTNER	LOCKER/DESK NO.	COURSE & SECTION NO.

SIGNATURE		DATE	WITNESS/TA		DATE

NOTE: INSERT DIVIDER UNDER COPY SHEET BEFORE WRITING

EXP. NUMBER	EXPERIMENT/SUBJECT		DATE	
NAME		LAB PARTNER	LOCKER/DESK NO.	COURSE & SECTION NO.

SIGNATURE		DATE	WITNESS/TA		DATE

NOTE: INSERT DIVIDER UNDER COPY SHEET BEFORE WRITING

SIGNATURE		DATE	WITNESS/TA		DATE

THE HAYDEN-McNEIL STUDENT LAB NOTEBOOK

NOTE: INSERT DIVIDER UNDER COPY SHEET BEFORE WRITING

EXP. NUMBER	EXPERIMENT/SUBJECT		DATE	
NAME		LAB PARTNER	LOCKER/DESK NO.	COURSE & SECTION NO.

SIGNATURE		DATE	WITNESS/TA		DATE

NOTE: INSERT DIVIDER UNDER COPY SHEET BEFORE WRITING

EXP. NUMBER	EXPERIMENT/SUBJECT		DATE	
NAME		LAB PARTNER	LOCKER/DESK NO.	COURSE & SECTION NO.

SIGNATURE		DATE	WITNESS/TA		DATE

NOTE: INSERT DIVIDER UNDER COPY SHEET BEFORE WRITING

SIGNATURE		DATE	WITNESS/TA		DATE

THE HAYDEN-McNEIL STUDENT LAB NOTEBOOK

NOTE: INSERT DIVIDER UNDER COPY SHEET BEFORE WRITING

EXP. NUMBER	EXPERIMENT/SUBJECT		DATE	
NAME		LAB PARTNER	LOCKER/DESK NO.	COURSE & SECTION NO.

SIGNATURE	DATE	WITNESS/TA	DATE

THE HAYDEN-McNEIL STUDENT LAB NOTEBOOK

NOTE: INSERT DIVIDER UNDER COPY SHEET BEFORE WRITING

EXP. NUMBER	EXPERIMENT/SUBJECT		DATE	
NAME		LAB PARTNER	LOCKER/DESK NO.	COURSE & SECTION NO.

SIGNATURE	DATE	WITNESS/TA	DATE

NOTE: INSERT DIVIDER UNDER COPY SHEET BEFORE WRITING

EXP. NUMBER	EXPERIMENT/SUBJECT		DATE	
NAME		LAB PARTNER	LOCKER/DESK NO.	COURSE & SECTION NO.

SIGNATURE	DATE	WITNESS/TA		DATE

NOTE: INSERT DIVIDER UNDER COPY SHEET BEFORE WRITING

EXP. NUMBER	EXPERIMENT/SUBJECT		DATE	
NAME		LAB PARTNER	LOCKER/DESK NO.	COURSE & SECTION NO.

SIGNATURE	DATE	WITNESS/TA	DATE

THE HAYDEN-McNEIL STUDENT LAB NOTEBOOK

NOTE: INSERT DIVIDER UNDER COPY SHEET BEFORE WRITING

EXP. NUMBER	EXPERIMENT/SUBJECT		DATE	50
NAME		LAB PARTNER	LOCKER/DESK NO.	COURSE & SECTION NO.

SIGNATURE		DATE	WITNESS/TA		DATE

NOTE: INSERT DIVIDER UNDER COPY SHEET BEFORE WRITING

EXP. NUMBER	EXPERIMENT/SUBJECT		DATE	
NAME		LAB PARTNER	LOCKER/DESK NO.	COURSE & SECTION NO.

SIGNATURE	DATE	WITNESS/TA	DATE

NOTE: INSERT DIVIDER UNDER COPY SHEET BEFORE WRITING

EXP. NUMBER	EXPERIMENT/SUBJECT		DATE	
NAME		LAB PARTNER	LOCKER/DESK NO.	COURSE & SECTION NO.

SIGNATURE		DATE	WITNESS/TA		DATE

NOTE: INSERT DIVIDER UNDER COPY SHEET BEFORE WRITING

EXP. NUMBER	EXPERIMENT/SUBJECT		DATE	
NAME		LAB PARTNER	LOCKER/DESK NO.	COURSE & SECTION NO.

SIGNATURE		DATE	WITNESS/TA		DATE

NOTE: INSERT DIVIDER UNDER COPY SHEET BEFORE WRITING

EXP. NUMBER	EXPERIMENT/SUBJECT		DATE		52
NAME		LAB PARTNER	LOCKER/DESK NO.	COURSE & SECTION NO.	

SIGNATURE		DATE	WITNESS/TA		DATE

THE HAYDEN-McNEIL STUDENT LAB NOTEBOOK

NOTE: INSERT DIVIDER UNDER COPY SHEET BEFORE WRITING

EXP. NUMBER	EXPERIMENT/SUBJECT		DATE	
NAME		LAB PARTNER	LOCKER/DESK NO.	COURSE & SECTION NO.

SIGNATURE	DATE	WITNESS/TA	DATE

NOTE: INSERT DIVIDER UNDER COPY SHEET BEFORE WRITING

EXP. NUMBER	EXPERIMENT/SUBJECT		DATE	
NAME		LAB PARTNER	LOCKER/DESK NO.	COURSE & SECTION NO.

SIGNATURE	DATE	WITNESS/TA	DATE

EXP. NUMBER	EXPERIMENT/SUBJECT		DATE	
NAME		LAB PARTNER	LOCKER/DESK NO.	COURSE & SECTION NO.

SIGNATURE	DATE	WITNESS/TA	DATE

NOTE: INSERT DIVIDER UNDER COPY SHEET BEFORE WRITING

EXP. NUMBER	EXPERIMENT/SUBJECT		DATE	
NAME		LAB PARTNER	LOCKER/DESK NO.	COURSE & SECTION NO.

SIGNATURE	DATE	WITNESS/TA	DATE

COPY

THE HAYDEN-McNEIL STUDENT LAB NOTEBOOK

NOTE: INSERT DIVIDER UNDER COPY SHEET BEFORE WRITING

EXP. NUMBER	EXPERIMENT/SUBJECT		DATE	
NAME		LAB PARTNER	LOCKER/DESK NO.	COURSE & SECTION NO.

SIGNATURE	DATE	WITNESS/TA	DATE

NOTE: INSERT DIVIDER UNDER COPY SHEET BEFORE WRITING

EXP. NUMBER	EXPERIMENT/SUBJECT		DATE	
NAME		LAB PARTNER	LOCKER/DESK NO.	COURSE & SECTION NO.

SIGNATURE	DATE	WITNESS/TA	DATE

THE HAYDEN-McNEIL STUDENT LAB NOTEBOOK

NOTE: INSERT DIVIDER UNDER COPY SHEET BEFORE WRITING

EXP. NUMBER	EXPERIMENT/SUBJECT		DATE	
NAME		LAB PARTNER	LOCKER/DESK NO.	COURSE & SECTION NO.

SIGNATURE	DATE	WITNESS/TA	DATE

NOTE: INSERT DIVIDER UNDER COPY SHEET BEFORE WRITING

EXP. NUMBER	EXPERIMENT/SUBJECT		DATE		58
NAME		LAB PARTNER	LOCKER/DESK NO.	COURSE & SECTION NO.	

SIGNATURE		DATE	WITNESS/TA		DATE

THE HAYDEN-McNEIL STUDENT LAB NOTEBOOK

NOTE: INSERT DIVIDER UNDER COPY SHEET BEFORE WRITING

EXP. NUMBER	EXPERIMENT/SUBJECT		DATE	
NAME		LAB PARTNER	LOCKER/DESK NO.	COURSE & SECTION NO.

SIGNATURE		DATE	WITNESS/TA		DATE

NOTE: INSERT DIVIDER UNDER COPY SHEET BEFORE WRITING

EXP. NUMBER	EXPERIMENT/SUBJECT		DATE	
NAME		LAB PARTNER	LOCKER/DESK NO.	COURSE & SECTION NO.

SIGNATURE	DATE	WITNESS/TA	DATE

THE HAYDEN-McNEIL STUDENT LAB NOTEBOOK

NOTE: INSERT DIVIDER UNDER COPY SHEET BEFORE WRITING

EXP. NUMBER	EXPERIMENT/SUBJECT		DATE	
NAME		LAB PARTNER	LOCKER/DESK NO.	COURSE & SECTION NO.

SIGNATURE	DATE	WITNESS/TA	DATE

EXP. NUMBER	EXPERIMENT/SUBJECT		DATE	
NAME		LAB PARTNER	LOCKER/DESK NO.	COURSE & SECTION NO.

SIGNATURE	DATE	WITNESS/TA	DATE

EXP. NUMBER	EXPERIMENT/SUBJECT		DATE	
NAME		LAB PARTNER	LOCKER/DESK NO.	COURSE & SECTION NO.

SIGNATURE		DATE	WITNESS/TA	DATE

NOTE: INSERT DIVIDER UNDER COPY SHEET BEFORE WRITING

EXP. NUMBER	EXPERIMENT/SUBJECT		DATE	
NAME		LAB PARTNER	LOCKER/DESK NO.	COURSE & SECTION NO.

SIGNATURE	DATE	WITNESS/TA		DATE

NOTE: INSERT DIVIDER UNDER COPY SHEET BEFORE WRITING

EXP. NUMBER	EXPERIMENT/SUBJECT		DATE	
NAME		LAB PARTNER	LOCKER/DESK NO.	COURSE & SECTION NO.

SIGNATURE	DATE	WITNESS/TA	DATE

EXP. NUMBER	EXPERIMENT/SUBJECT		DATE	
NAME		LAB PARTNER	LOCKER/DESK NO.	COURSE & SECTION NO.

SIGNATURE	DATE	WITNESS/TA	DATE

THE HAYDEN-McNEIL STUDENT LAB NOTEBOOK

NOTE: INSERT DIVIDER UNDER COPY SHEET BEFORE WRITING

EXP. NUMBER	EXPERIMENT/SUBJECT		DATE	
NAME		LAB PARTNER	LOCKER/DESK NO.	COURSE & SECTION NO.

SIGNATURE	DATE	WITNESS/TA	DATE

NOTE: INSERT DIVIDER UNDER COPY SHEET BEFORE WRITING

EXP. NUMBER	EXPERIMENT/SUBJECT		DATE	
NAME		LAB PARTNER	LOCKER/DESK NO.	COURSE & SECTION NO.

SIGNATURE	DATE	WITNESS/TA	DATE

NOTE: INSERT DIVIDER UNDER COPY SHEET BEFORE WRITING

EXP. NUMBER	EXPERIMENT/SUBJECT		DATE	
NAME		LAB PARTNER	LOCKER/DESK NO.	COURSE & SECTION NO.

SIGNATURE	DATE	WITNESS/TA	DATE

NOTE: INSERT DIVIDER UNDER COPY SHEET BEFORE WRITING

EXP. NUMBER	EXPERIMENT/SUBJECT		DATE	
NAME		LAB PARTNER	LOCKER/DESK NO.	COURSE & SECTION NO.

SIGNATURE	DATE	WITNESS/TA	DATE

THE HAYDEN-McNEIL STUDENT LAB NOTEBOOK

NOTE: INSERT DIVIDER UNDER COPY SHEET BEFORE WRITING

EXP. NUMBER	EXPERIMENT/SUBJECT	DATE	

NAME	LAB PARTNER	LOCKER/DESK NO.	COURSE & SECTION NO.

SIGNATURE	DATE	WITNESS/TA	DATE

NOTE: INSERT DIVIDER UNDER COPY SHEET BEFORE WRITING

EXP. NUMBER	EXPERIMENT/SUBJECT		DATE		66
NAME		LAB PARTNER	LOCKER/DESK NO.	COURSE & SECTION NO.	

SIGNATURE	DATE	WITNESS/TA	DATE

THE HAYDEN-McNEIL STUDENT LAB NOTEBOOK

NOTE: INSERT DIVIDER UNDER COPY SHEET BEFORE WRITING

EXP. NUMBER	EXPERIMENT/SUBJECT		DATE	
NAME		LAB PARTNER	LOCKER/DESK NO.	COURSE & SECTION NO.

SIGNATURE	DATE	WITNESS/TA	DATE

EXP. NUMBER	EXPERIMENT/SUBJECT		DATE	
NAME		LAB PARTNER	LOCKER/DESK NO.	COURSE & SECTION NO.

SIGNATURE	DATE	WITNESS/TA	DATE

NOTE: INSERT DIVIDER UNDER COPY SHEET BEFORE WRITING

EXP. NUMBER	EXPERIMENT/SUBJECT		DATE	
NAME		LAB PARTNER	LOCKER/DESK NO.	COURSE & SECTION NO.

SIGNATURE		DATE	WITNESS/TA		DATE

EXP. NUMBER	EXPERIMENT/SUBJECT		DATE	
NAME		LAB PARTNER	LOCKER/DESK NO.	COURSE & SECTION NO.

SIGNATURE	DATE	WITNESS/TA	DATE

NOTE: INSERT DIVIDER UNDER COPY SHEET BEFORE WRITING

EXP. NUMBER	EXPERIMENT/SUBJECT		DATE	
NAME		LAB PARTNER	LOCKER/DESK NO.	COURSE & SECTION NO.

SIGNATURE	DATE	WITNESS/TA	DATE

NOTE: INSERT DIVIDER UNDER COPY SHEET BEFORE WRITING

EXP. NUMBER	EXPERIMENT/SUBJECT		DATE		70
NAME		LAB PARTNER	LOCKER/DESK NO.	COURSE & SECTION NO.	

COPY

SIGNATURE	DATE	WITNESS/TA		DATE

NOTE: INSERT DIVIDER UNDER COPY SHEET BEFORE WRITING

EXP. NUMBER	EXPERIMENT/SUBJECT		DATE	
NAME		LAB PARTNER	LOCKER/DESK NO.	COURSE & SECTION NO.

SIGNATURE	DATE	WITNESS/TA	DATE

NOTE: INSERT DIVIDER UNDER COPY SHEET BEFORE WRITING

EXP. NUMBER	EXPERIMENT/SUBJECT		DATE	
NAME		LAB PARTNER	LOCKER/DESK NO.	COURSE & SECTION NO.

SIGNATURE	DATE	WITNESS/TA	DATE

NOTE: INSERT DIVIDER UNDER COPY SHEET BEFORE WRITING

EXP. NUMBER	EXPERIMENT/SUBJECT		DATE	
NAME		LAB PARTNER	LOCKER/DESK NO.	COURSE & SECTION NO.

SIGNATURE	DATE	WITNESS/TA	DATE

NOTE: INSERT DIVIDER UNDER COPY SHEET BEFORE WRITING

EXP. NUMBER	EXPERIMENT/SUBJECT		DATE	
NAME		LAB PARTNER	LOCKER/DESK NO.	COURSE & SECTION NO.

SIGNATURE		DATE	WITNESS/TA		DATE

NOTE: INSERT DIVIDER UNDER COPY SHEET BEFORE WRITING

EXP. NUMBER	EXPERIMENT/SUBJECT		DATE	
NAME		LAB PARTNER	LOCKER/DESK NO.	COURSE & SECTION NO.

SIGNATURE	DATE	WITNESS/TA	DATE

THE HAYDEN-McNEIL STUDENT LAB NOTEBOOK

NOTE: INSERT DIVIDER UNDER COPY SHEET BEFORE WRITING

EXP. NUMBER	EXPERIMENT/SUBJECT		DATE	
NAME		LAB PARTNER	LOCKER/DESK NO.	COURSE & SECTION NO.

SIGNATURE	DATE	WITNESS/TA	DATE

NOTE: INSERT DIVIDER UNDER COPY SHEET BEFORE WRITING

EXP. NUMBER	EXPERIMENT/SUBJECT		DATE	
NAME		LAB PARTNER	LOCKER/DESK NO.	COURSE & SECTION NO.

SIGNATURE	DATE	WITNESS/TA	DATE

THE HAYDEN-McNEIL STUDENT LAB NOTEBOOK

NOTE: INSERT DIVIDER UNDER COPY SHEET BEFORE WRITING

EXP. NUMBER	EXPERIMENT/SUBJECT		DATE	
NAME		LAB PARTNER	LOCKER/DESK NO.	COURSE & SECTION NO.

SIGNATURE	DATE	WITNESS/TA	DATE

THE HAYDEN-McNEIL STUDENT LAB NOTEBOOK

NOTE: INSERT DIVIDER UNDER COPY SHEET BEFORE WRITING

EXP. NUMBER	EXPERIMENT/SUBJECT		DATE	
NAME		LAB PARTNER	LOCKER/DESK NO.	COURSE & SECTION NO.

SIGNATURE	DATE	WITNESS/TA	DATE

THE HAYDEN-McNEIL STUDENT LAB NOTEBOOK

NOTE: INSERT DIVIDER UNDER COPY SHEET BEFORE WRITING

EXP. NUMBER	EXPERIMENT/SUBJECT		DATE	
NAME		LAB PARTNER	LOCKER/DESK NO.	COURSE & SECTION NO.

SIGNATURE		DATE	WITNESS/TA		DATE

THE HAYDEN-McNEIL STUDENT LAB NOTEBOOK

NOTE: INSERT DIVIDER UNDER COPY SHEET BEFORE WRITING

EXP. NUMBER	EXPERIMENT/SUBJECT		DATE	
NAME		LAB PARTNER	LOCKER/DESK NO.	COURSE & SECTION NO.

SIGNATURE	DATE	WITNESS/TA	DATE

NOTE: INSERT DIVIDER UNDER COPY SHEET BEFORE WRITING

EXP. NUMBER	EXPERIMENT/SUBJECT		DATE		77
NAME		LAB PARTNER	LOCKER/DESK NO.	COURSE & SECTION NO.	

COPY

SIGNATURE	DATE	WITNESS/TA	DATE

THE HAYDEN-McNEIL STUDENT LAB NOTEBOOK

NOTE: INSERT DIVIDER UNDER COPY SHEET BEFORE WRITING

EXP. NUMBER	EXPERIMENT/SUBJECT		DATE	78
NAME		LAB PARTNER	LOCKER/DESK NO.	COURSE & SECTION NO.

SIGNATURE	DATE	WITNESS/TA		DATE

THE HAYDEN-McNEIL STUDENT LAB NOTEBOOK

NOTE: INSERT DIVIDER UNDER COPY SHEET BEFORE WRITING

EXP. NUMBER	EXPERIMENT/SUBJECT		DATE	
NAME		LAB PARTNER	LOCKER/DESK NO.	COURSE & SECTION NO.

SIGNATURE	DATE	WITNESS/TA	DATE

NOTE: INSERT DIVIDER UNDER COPY SHEET BEFORE WRITING

EXP. NUMBER	EXPERIMENT/SUBJECT		DATE	
NAME		LAB PARTNER	LOCKER/DESK NO.	COURSE & SECTION NO.

SIGNATURE		DATE	WITNESS/TA		DATE

THE HAYDEN-McNEIL STUDENT LAB NOTEBOOK

NOTE: INSERT DIVIDER UNDER COPY SHEET BEFORE WRITING

THE HAYDEN-McNEIL STUDENT LAB NOTEBOOK

NOTE: INSERT DIVIDER UNDER COPY SHEET BEFORE WRITING

EXP. NUMBER	EXPERIMENT/SUBJECT		DATE	80
NAME		LAB PARTNER	LOCKER/DESK NO.	COURSE & SECTION NO.

SIGNATURE	DATE	WITNESS/TA	DATE

THE HAYDEN-McNEIL STUDENT LAB NOTEBOOK

NOTE: INSERT DIVIDER UNDER COPY SHEET BEFORE WRITING

EXP. NUMBER	EXPERIMENT/SUBJECT		DATE		81
NAME		LAB PARTNER	LOCKER/DESK NO.	COURSE & SECTION NO.	

SIGNATURE		DATE	WITNESS/TA		DATE

THE HAYDEN-McNEIL STUDENT LAB NOTEBOOK

NOTE: INSERT DIVIDER UNDER COPY SHEET BEFORE WRITING

EXP. NUMBER	EXPERIMENT/SUBJECT		DATE	
NAME		LAB PARTNER	LOCKER/DESK NO.	COURSE & SECTION NO.

SIGNATURE		DATE	WITNESS/TA		DATE

NOTE: INSERT DIVIDER UNDER COPY SHEET BEFORE WRITING

THE HAYDEN-McNEIL STUDENT LAB NOTEBOOK

NOTE: INSERT DIVIDER UNDER COPY SHEET BEFORE WRITING

EXP. NUMBER	EXPERIMENT/SUBJECT		DATE		82
NAME		LAB PARTNER	LOCKER/DESK NO.	COURSE & SECTION NO.	

SIGNATURE		DATE	WITNESS/TA		DATE

THE HAYDEN-McNEIL STUDENT LAB NOTEBOOK

NOTE: INSERT DIVIDER UNDER COPY SHEET BEFORE WRITING

EXP. NUMBER	EXPERIMENT/SUBJECT		DATE	
NAME		LAB PARTNER	LOCKER/DESK NO.	COURSE & SECTION NO.

SIGNATURE	DATE	WITNESS/TA	DATE

NOTE: INSERT DIVIDER UNDER COPY SHEET BEFORE WRITING

EXP. NUMBER	EXPERIMENT/SUBJECT		DATE	
NAME		LAB PARTNER	LOCKER/DESK NO.	COURSE & SECTION NO.

COPY

SIGNATURE		DATE	WITNESS/TA		DATE

NOTE: INSERT DIVIDER UNDER COPY SHEET BEFORE WRITING

EXP. NUMBER	EXPERIMENT/SUBJECT		DATE	
NAME		LAB PARTNER	LOCKER/DESK NO.	COURSE & SECTION NO.

SIGNATURE	DATE	WITNESS/TA	DATE

NOTE: INSERT DIVIDER UNDER COPY SHEET BEFORE WRITING

EXP. NUMBER	EXPERIMENT/SUBJECT		DATE	
NAME		LAB PARTNER	LOCKER/DESK NO.	COURSE & SECTION NO.

SIGNATURE		DATE	WITNESS/TA		DATE

NOTE: INSERT DIVIDER UNDER COPY SHEET BEFORE WRITING

EXP. NUMBER	EXPERIMENT/SUBJECT		DATE	
NAME		LAB PARTNER	LOCKER/DESK NO.	COURSE & SECTION NO.

SIGNATURE		DATE	WITNESS/TA		DATE

EXP. NUMBER	EXPERIMENT/SUBJECT		DATE	
NAME		LAB PARTNER	LOCKER/DESK NO.	COURSE & SECTION NO.

SIGNATURE	DATE	WITNESS/TA	DATE

NOTE: INSERT DIVIDER UNDER COPY SHEET BEFORE WRITING

EXP. NUMBER	EXPERIMENT/SUBJECT		DATE	
NAME		LAB PARTNER	LOCKER/DESK NO.	COURSE & SECTION NO.

SIGNATURE		DATE	WITNESS/TA	DATE

NOTE: INSERT DIVIDER UNDER COPY SHEET BEFORE WRITING

EXP. NUMBER	EXPERIMENT/SUBJECT		DATE		88
NAME		LAB PARTNER	LOCKER/DESK NO.	COURSE & SECTION NO.	

SIGNATURE		DATE	WITNESS/TA		DATE

THE HAYDEN-McNEIL STUDENT LAB NOTEBOOK

NOTE: INSERT DIVIDER UNDER COPY SHEET BEFORE WRITING

EXP. NUMBER	EXPERIMENT/SUBJECT		DATE	
NAME		LAB PARTNER	LOCKER/DESK NO.	COURSE & SECTION NO.

SIGNATURE	DATE	WITNESS/TA	DATE

NOTE: INSERT DIVIDER UNDER COPY SHEET BEFORE WRITING

EXP. NUMBER	EXPERIMENT/SUBJECT		DATE	
NAME		LAB PARTNER	LOCKER/DESK NO.	COURSE & SECTION NO.

SIGNATURE	DATE	WITNESS/TA	DATE

NOTE: INSERT DIVIDER UNDER COPY SHEET BEFORE WRITING

EXP. NUMBER	EXPERIMENT/SUBJECT		DATE	
NAME		LAB PARTNER	LOCKER/DESK NO.	COURSE & SECTION NO.

SIGNATURE		DATE	WITNESS/TA		DATE

NOTE: INSERT DIVIDER UNDER COPY SHEET BEFORE WRITING

EXP. NUMBER	EXPERIMENT/SUBJECT		DATE	
NAME		LAB PARTNER	LOCKER/DESK NO.	COURSE & SECTION NO.

SIGNATURE		DATE	WITNESS/TA		DATE

NOTE: INSERT DIVIDER UNDER COPY SHEET BEFORE WRITING

EXP. NUMBER	EXPERIMENT/SUBJECT		DATE	
NAME		LAB PARTNER	LOCKER/DESK NO.	COURSE & SECTION NO.

SIGNATURE		DATE	WITNESS/TA		DATE

THE HAYDEN-McNEIL STUDENT LAB NOTEBOOK

NOTE: INSERT DIVIDER UNDER COPY SHEET BEFORE WRITING

EXP. NUMBER	EXPERIMENT/SUBJECT		DATE	
NAME		LAB PARTNER	LOCKER/DESK NO.	COURSE & SECTION NO.

SIGNATURE		DATE	WITNESS/TA		DATE

NOTE: INSERT DIVIDER UNDER COPY SHEET BEFORE WRITING

EXP. NUMBER	EXPERIMENT/SUBJECT		DATE	
NAME		LAB PARTNER	LOCKER/DESK NO.	COURSE & SECTION NO.

SIGNATURE	DATE	WITNESS/TA	DATE

NOTE: INSERT DIVIDER UNDER COPY SHEET BEFORE WRITING

EXP. NUMBER	EXPERIMENT/SUBJECT		DATE	
NAME		LAB PARTNER	LOCKER/DESK NO.	COURSE & SECTION NO.

SIGNATURE		DATE	WITNESS/TA		DATE

NOTE: INSERT DIVIDER UNDER COPY SHEET BEFORE WRITING

EXP. NUMBER	EXPERIMENT/SUBJECT		DATE	
NAME		LAB PARTNER	LOCKER/DESK NO.	COURSE & SECTION NO.

SIGNATURE		DATE	WITNESS/TA		DATE

NOTE: INSERT DIVIDER UNDER COPY SHEET BEFORE WRITING

EXP. NUMBER	EXPERIMENT/SUBJECT		DATE	
NAME		LAB PARTNER	LOCKER/DESK NO.	COURSE & SECTION NO.

SIGNATURE	DATE	WITNESS/TA		DATE

NOTE: INSERT DIVIDER UNDER COPY SHEET BEFORE WRITING

EXP. NUMBER	EXPERIMENT/SUBJECT		DATE	
NAME		LAB PARTNER	LOCKER/DESK NO.	COURSE & SECTION NO.

SIGNATURE	DATE	WITNESS/TA	DATE

EXP. NUMBER	EXPERIMENT/SUBJECT		DATE	
NAME		LAB PARTNER	LOCKER/DESK NO.	COURSE & SECTION NO.

SIGNATURE	DATE	WITNESS/TA	DATE

NOTE: INSERT DIVIDER UNDER COPY SHEET BEFORE WRITING

EXP. NUMBER	EXPERIMENT/SUBJECT		DATE	
NAME		LAB PARTNER	LOCKER/DESK NO.	COURSE & SECTION NO.

SIGNATURE		DATE	WITNESS/TA		DATE

THE HAYDEN-McNEIL STUDENT LAB NOTEBOOK

NOTE: INSERT DIVIDER UNDER COPY SHEET BEFORE WRITING

EXP. NUMBER	EXPERIMENT/SUBJECT		DATE	
NAME		LAB PARTNER	LOCKER/DESK NO.	COURSE & SECTION NO.

SIGNATURE		DATE	WITNESS/TA		DATE

EXP. NUMBER	EXPERIMENT/SUBJECT		DATE	
NAME		LAB PARTNER	LOCKER/DESK NO.	COURSE & SECTION NO.

SIGNATURE	DATE	WITNESS/TA	DATE

NOTE: INSERT DIVIDER UNDER COPY SHEET BEFORE WRITING

EXP. NUMBER	EXPERIMENT/SUBJECT		DATE	
NAME		LAB PARTNER	LOCKER/DESK NO.	COURSE & SECTION NO.

SIGNATURE	DATE	WITNESS/TA	DATE

THE HAYDEN-McNEIL STUDENT LAB NOTEBOOK

NOTE: INSERT DIVIDER UNDER COPY SHEET BEFORE WRITING

EXP. NUMBER	EXPERIMENT/SUBJECT		DATE	
NAME		LAB PARTNER	LOCKER/DESK NO.	COURSE & SECTION NO.

SIGNATURE	DATE	WITNESS/TA	DATE

EXP. NUMBER	EXPERIMENT/SUBJECT		DATE	
NAME		LAB PARTNER	LOCKER/DESK NO.	COURSE & SECTION NO.

COPY

SIGNATURE	DATE	WITNESS/TA	DATE

THE HAYDEN-McNEIL STUDENT LAB NOTEBOOK

NOTE: INSERT DIVIDER UNDER COPY SHEET BEFORE WRITING

SECTION: B IMAGING

BODY SYSTEM: 9 EAR, NOSE, MOUTH, AND THROAT

TYPE: Ø **PLAIN RADIOGRAPHY:** Planar display of an image developed from the capture of external ionizing radiation on photographic or photoconductive plate

Body Part	Contrast	Qualifier	Qualifier
2 Paranasal Sinuses F Nasopharynx/Oropharynx H Mastoids	Z None	Z None	Z None
4 Parotid Gland, Right 5 Parotid Gland, Left 6 Parotid Glands, Bilateral 7 Submandibular Gland, Right 8 Submandibular Gland, Left 9 Submandibular Glands, Bilateral B Salivary Gland, Right C Salivary Gland, Left D Salivary Glands, Bilateral	Ø High Osmolar 1 Low Osmolar Y Other Contrast	Z None	Z None

SECTION: B IMAGING

BODY SYSTEM: 9 EAR, NOSE, MOUTH, AND THROAT

TYPE: 1 **FLUOROSCOPY:** Single plane or bi-plane real time display of an image developed from the capture of external ionizing radiation on a fluorescent screen. The image may also be stored by either digital or analog means

Body Part	Contrast	Qualifier	Qualifier
G Pharynx and Epiglottis J Larynx	Y Other Contrast Z None	Z None	Z None

SECTION: **B IMAGING**

BODY SYSTEM: 9 **EAR, NOSE, MOUTH, AND THROAT**

TYPE: 2 **COMPUTERIZED TOMOGRAPHY (CT SCAN):** Computer reformatted digital display of multiplanar images developed from the capture of multiple exposures of external ionizing radiation

Body Part	Contrast	Qualifier	Qualifier
Ø Ear 2 Paranasal Sinuses 6 Parotid Glands, Bilateral 9 Submandibular Glands, Bilateral D Salivary Glands, Bilateral F Nasopharynx/Oropharynx J Larynx	Ø High Osmolar 1 Low Osmolar Y Other Contrast	Ø Unenhanced and Enhanced Z None	Z None
Ø Ear 2 Paranasal Sinuses 6 Parotid Glands, Bilateral 9 Submandibular Glands, Bilateral D Salivary Glands, Bilateral F Nasopharynx/Oropharynx J Larynx	Z None	Z None	Z None

SECTION: **B IMAGING**

BODY SYSTEM: 9 **EAR, NOSE, MOUTH, AND THROAT**

TYPE: 3 **MAGNETIC RESONANCE IMAGING (MRI):** Computer reformatted digital display of multiplanar images developed from the capture of radiofrequency signals emitted by nuclei in a body site excited within a magnetic field

Body Part	Contrast	Qualifier	Qualifier
Ø Ear 2 Paranasal Sinuses 6 Parotid Glands, Bilateral 9 Submandibular Glands, Bilateral D Salivary Glands, Bilateral F Nasopharynx/Oropharynx J Larynx	Y Other Contrast	Ø Unenhanced and Enhanced Z None	Z None
Ø Ear 2 Paranasal Sinuses 6 Parotid Glands, Bilateral 9 Submandibular Glands, Bilateral D Salivary Glands, Bilateral F Nasopharynx/Oropharynx J Larynx	Z None	Z None	Z None

(Side tab: 2: CT SCAN   3: MRI)

(Side tab: 9: EAR, NOSE, MOUTH, AND THROAT)

(Side tab: B: IMAGING)

New/Revised Text in Green   ~~deleted~~ Deleted   ♀ Females Only   ♂ Males Only   **Coding Clinic**

🅠 Non-covered   🅠 Limited Coverage   ⊕ Combination (See Appendix E)   DRG Non-OR   Non-OR   🅠 Hospital-Acquired Condition